TO RAINN, LANDSEA,
AND COLORADO. I
STILL HAVE MIXED
FEELINGS ABOUT
YOU, COLORADO.

DAVID

FOR HER.

DANNY

FOR THE
QUIET KIDS.
IT WILL GET
BETTER.

LINDSAY

TETHERED

STORY – DAVID FAROZ PRECHT

ART – DANNY LUCKERT

LETTERING / LAYOUT – LINDSAY MCCOMB

EDITING – JOANNE STARER

CREATED BY

DAVID FAROZ PRECHT AND DANNY LUCKERT

TETHEREDCOMIC.COM

CHAPTER ONE:
NUMBNESS

AT THE MOMENT

I DIED A WEEK AGO. OR TWO MAYBE. I DON'T KNOW.

ONE SECOND I WAS THERE, THE NEXT I WASN'T.

IT'S NOT AS CLEAR AS IT ONCE WAS. DIDN'T HAVE A FUNERAL – THANKS FOR THAT BY THE WAY. NO ONE SEEMED TO CARE.

MAYBE IT WAS TWO WEEKS AGO.

I WATCH IT RUN.

MY BODY.

IT ALWAYS DID HUNGER FOR MORE.

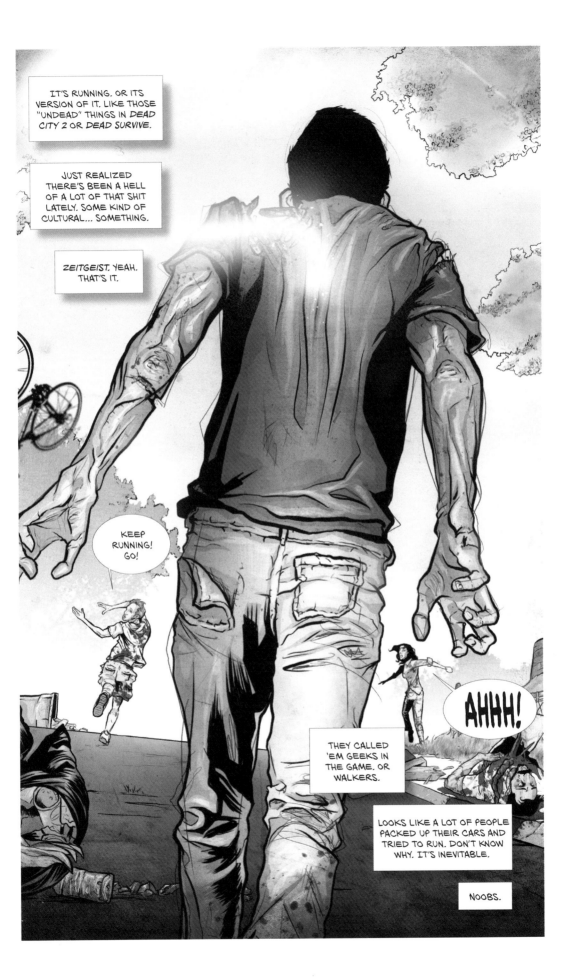

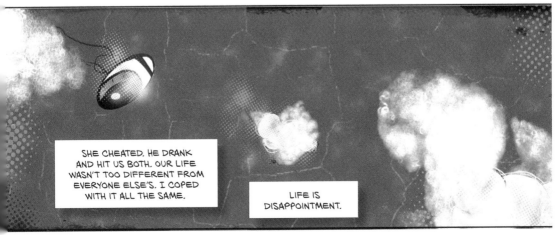

TEN YEARS OLD

EITHER WAY, IT WAS ENTERTAINING WHILE IT LASTED.

MARVIN LORREY:
1958 - 1994

FAMOUS TV DAD COMMITS SUICIDE

DAD'S HOUSE WAS GONE, SO I MOVED ON. THAT SEEMS TO BE THE WAY OF THINGS. THINGS ARE ALL RIGHT FOR AWHILE, THEN THEY'RE NOT. CONSISTENCY DOESN'T EXIST.

THERE WOULD ALWAYS BE BRUISES TO PUT ICE ON, AND THERE WOULD ALWAYS BE NEW DISTRACTIONS. TV TO ATARI. ATARI TO SEGA. SEGA TO XBOX. AND SO ON.

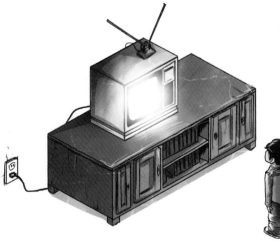

THERE WOULD BE FEAR. AND THERE WOULD BE FUEL.

ALWAYS TOO MANY
MEMBERS OF THE CULT
OF EXERCISE ASKING WHY
I WASN'T OUT TOO. FOR
EVERY SHIT I GAVE, THEY
GAVE A THOUSAND. *MORONS.*

SOME OF THE DEAD THINGS
SURROUND MY OLD BODY,
LIKE THEY'RE A CLAN, AND
IT LOOKS LIKE MY OLD BODY
IS THE LEADER OF THE
CLAN. OR WHATEVER.

CLAN OLD
BODIES. *HEH.*

THE DAY CONTINUES
AND ANOTHER
MEMBER IS
ADDED TO MY OLD
BODY'S CLAN.

THERE'S A SOUND... LIKE
SOMEONE TOUCHING
A HEADPHONE PLUG
TO THE SIDES OF A
HEADPHONE JACK.

CHAPTER TWO:
STRENGTH

AT THE MOMENT

I REALIZED I COULD CONTROL MY BODY, NOT LONG AFTER I DIED.

WHAT THE FUCK'S UP, BITCHES?

I HAD BEEN INTOXICATED THE NIGHT BEFORE. LONG STORY SHORT, IT WAS UPLIFTING AND SHE HAD A RADIANT PERSONALITY. THEN, I WAS DEAD.

GET ME DRUNK. GET ME DRUNK.

BUT LET'S NOT DEBASE OURSELVES WITH SUCH STORIES.

THE PURPOSE OF LIFE IS TO BE POSITIVE, AFTER ALL. THE EMBODIMENT OF COMPASSION AND LOVE, THE DALAI LAMA SAID THAT. SO I'VE FOCUSED MY ATTENTIONS THUSLY.

WHY WON'T YOU FUCKING GET ME DRUNK? DO YOUR JOB.

NOTHING. NOT A **DAMN** THING.

I NEVER THOUGHT MY CYCLICAL REBIRTH WOULD TAKE THE SHAPE OF THIS EMBODIMENT OF ACTION, BUT I NOW REALIZE HOW UTTERLY PERFECT, BASED ON MY OWN PERSONAL PHILOSOPHY, IT IS.

SOME MIGHT SAY THAT A DAREDEVIL'S JOB IS TO TRY TO COMMIT SUICIDE EVERYDAY.

I DISAGREE.

HE **MADE** IT! I CAN'T BELIEVE IT!!

DAREDEVILS ARE THE EMBODIMENT OF MAN. OF HUMANITY. THEY LIVE FEARLESSLY WHILE THE REST OF YOU COVER YOUR EYES.

...VER SEEN **ANYTHING** LIKE THAT IN MY LIFETIME!!

"EVERY MAN'S LIFE ENDS THE SAME WAY. IT IS ONLY THE DETAILS OF HOW HE LIVED AND HOW HE DIED THAT DISTINGUISH ONE MAN FROM ANOTHER."

I READ DAD SOME HEMINGWAY. WELL, I GAVE HIM THE CLIFF NOTES.

HIS FAVORITE, AND MINE, WAS *THE SUN ALSO RISES*.

HE WOULD ASK ME TO READ, DIRECTLY, FROM THE BULL FIGHT SCENES, AND TOLD ME HE'D HAVE DREAMS ABOUT BULL FIGHTING.

HE'D WAKE UP SCREAMING, SWEATING, HIS PULSE RACING. I GUESS LUCID DREAMS RUN IN THE FAMILY.

FOR ME, IT WAS THE DAREDEVIL I SAW AT FIVE. HE CLEARED BUSES WITH SUCH EASE AND RECEIVED SUCH AN IMPASSIONED RESPONSE, THAT IT KICK-STARTED MY NEED FOR MORE.

MY DREAM SHOWED ME WHAT I WOULD NEED TO BECOME: ACTION PERSONIFIED.

AND IT WAS ALL BECAUSE DAD SHOWED ME WHAT HIS LIFE WAS LIKE: FEARLESS. ADRENALINE-FILLED.

A LIFE WELL LIVED.

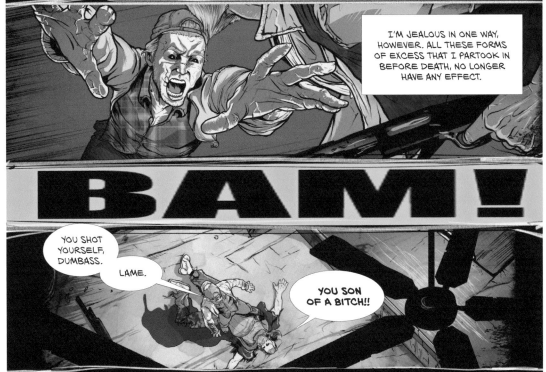

CHAPTER THREE:
WHISPERS

IN THE PAST

MAMAN WAS FORTY-THREE AND STILL SEARCHING. KIND OF PATHETIC, REALLY.

A MIDDLE-AGED GRAD STUDENT AT THE COMPUTER LAB IN GIFFORD ASKED ME ONCE IF MAMAN WAS HOT, WHILE WE WERE REPLACING A SPOOL OF PAPER.

SHE WAS, I TOLD HIM. I GUESS THAT WAS THE RIGHT ANSWER BECAUSE HE LEFT ME ALONE AFTER THAT.

SHE CALLED ME. THE NIGHT BEFORE I DIED, I THINK. SHE MENTIONED THAT SHE WAS SEEING SOMEONE NEW AND "GETTING HELP."

IN THE PAST

SHE ALWAYS HAD THIS WAY OF, LIKE, HESITATING WHEN SHE TALKED ABOUT MEN. BUT SHE TALKED ABOUT THIS NEW GUY.

A LOT.

LOOKS LIKE A DESIGN BLOG THREW UP IN HERE. I DON'T KNOW WHY MARIE GOT US ALL THIS FURNITURE. I DON'T EVEN USE IT.

SO THE GUY GAVE HER FLOWERS...

HER CONVERSATIONS ABOUT MEN WERE LIKE LOVE NOTES IN MIDDLE SCHOOL LOCKERS. SHE MUST HAVE BEEN IN LOVE WITH, LIKE, FORTY GUYS.

GOD, SHE TALKS A LOT.

I USUALLY JUST LET HER KEEP TALKING IN THESE SITUATIONS...

SHE NEVER NOTICES ANYWAY, SO IT DIDN'T MATTER.

I TOLD HER IT WOULDN'T LAST. HER AND THE NEW DORK. IT NEVER DID. SHE DIDN'T RESPOND.

REALITY HURTS.

I TOLD HER THAT'S JUST THE WAY THINGS WERE, THAT IT'S JUST HOW LIFE IS.

SHE DISAGREED, WHICH WAS NEW, AND TOLD ME SHE THOUGHT THAT LIFE REQUIRED ACTION.

SLEEPY.

SHE ASKED ME IF I WANTED TO COME VISIT NEXT WEEKEND. I TOLD HER I DIDN'T KNOW, BUT PROBABLY NOT.

SHE DIDN'T SAY ANYTHING. THEN, SHE TOLD ME SHE HAD TO GO.

CHAPTER FOUR:
UNFOUND

IN THE PAST

ONE YEAR EARLIER

OF WICKEDNESS, I CAN ONLY SAY THIS: IT IS A LEARNED BEHAVIOR. SCIENCE EXPLAINS IT THIS WAY.

AH, BASEBALL: ALL THE BOREDOM OF REAL LIFE WITH ALL THE LIMITLESS BEER YOU'D HOPE LIFE WAS FULL OF.

NO CREATURE IS SPAWNED AS THE AVATAR OF EVIL. THERE ARE STAGES THROUGHOUT OUR LIVES WHERE WE MAKE THE CHOICE TO BE ANGELS OR DEVILS.

HOW ELSE COULD ANYONE MAKE IT TILL THE LAST INNING?

ONE YEAR EARLIER

NOT TOO HOPPY FOR YOU?

JUST FINE.

NOT WATCHING THE GAME?

"THERE IS NO HUNTING LIKE THE HUNTING OF MAN, AND THOSE WHO HAVE HUNTED ARMED MEN LONG ENOUGH AND LIKED IT, NEVER CARE FOR ANYTHING ELSE THEREAFTER." THAT'S HEMINGWAY AGAIN, IF YOU WERE WONDERING.

LONG DAY?

WOULD YOU LIKE TO JOIN...

NOPE.

THE MAN WAS FULL OF POIGNANT FACTS THAT SEEM CHERRY-PICKED FOR MY EVERY SITUATION.

HEY, BUDDY. SHE DON'T COME HERE TO GET PICKED UP ON.

I CAN IMAGINE MEN AFTER THE GREAT WAR, SITTING IN CAFES IN FRANCE, COMPARING THEIR WAR WOUNDS. THEY WERE MEN, BUT GREAT MEN WERE FORGED FROM TRENCHFOOT AND BATTLE. WAR BROUGHT ON EVOLUTION.

IF NOT FOR WAR, THE STRONG WOULDN'T BECOME THE PREVAILING POWER.

"I AM OPEN TO THE GUIDANCE OF SYNCHRONICITY, AND DO NOT LET EXPECTATIONS HINDER MY PATH."

THAT CERTAINLY DOESN'T MEAN I DON'T GET FRUSTRATED.

AH, I REALIZE I USED A DOUBLE NEGATIVE THERE AND SHOULD CLARIFY: I GET FRUSTRATED, BUT NOT FOR LONG.

WHY ARE YOU FUCKING RUNNING? I'M TRYING TO HELP YOU!

I'M SURE IF SOME JERK... ER...SOUL WERE TO... OPPRESS HIS HOLINESS, HE WOULD EXHIBIT SOME FORM OF FRUSTRATION.

BUT THIS WAS MY FAULT.

I WILL WILLFULLY ADMIT THAT. I SHOULD NOT HAVE EXPECTED THOSE TIRED, HUDDLED MASSES TO THROW THEMSELVES AT MY FEET.

THEY'VE LIVED IN CHAOS FOR A LONG TIME. TO SEE A BEING SHIMMERING AND ABLE TO DELIVER THEM FROM SAID CHAOS IS JARRING.

DAMMIT. SHE HAD THAT OUTDOORSY BODY.

LET'S JUST HOPE THAT OUR NEXT MEETING GOES BETTER.

CHAPTER FIVE:
SOMETHING

AT THE MOMENT

I GREW UP OUTSIDE OF DENVER – THAT TOWN PEOPLE DELUDE THEMSELVES INTO BELIEVING IS A CITY – IN UNINCORPORATED AND PROUD EDGEWATER.

THE NUMBER ONE CONVERSATION STARTER IN COLORADO WAS THE RAIN – THE RAIN OR THE SNOWPACK.

THEY'D IGNORE EACH OTHER ANY OTHER TIME, LIVING THEIR ISOLATED, OUTDOORSY LIVES. BUT THEY SHARED THAT ONE FUCKING MOMENT, THAT WAVE GOOD-BYE, AND WON'T SPEAK TO EACH OTHER AGAIN UNTIL THE NEXT TIME RAIN MIGHT COME, WEEKS LATER.

LOOK AT ME! I'M HUMAN! SEE!

MORONS.

THEY'RE A PERFECT MATCH, THESE DEAD THINGS AND THE FORMER LIVING. NO BRAINS. LIKE ROBOTS, DOING WHAT THEY'RE TOLD.

I WONDER IF THESE THINGS BELIEVE IN WHAT THEY'RE DOING. EATING PEOPLE. OR ARE THEY JUST DOING IT? IS IT PROGRAMMING THAT KEEPS THEM LOOKING FOR FOOD?

GO FOR A RUN AT LUNCH. GLUTEN-FREE SANDWICH. VEGAN POT BROWNIES. FIFTEEN-MILE BIKE RIDE BACK TO THEIR HOUSE IN BOULDER.

FUCK YOU, FREE WILL. GIVE US OUR PROGRAMMING.

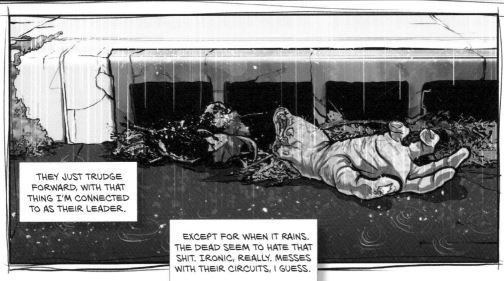

THEY JUST TRUDGE FORWARD, WITH THAT THING I'M CONNECTED TO AS THEIR LEADER.

EXCEPT FOR WHEN IT RAINS. THE DEAD SEEM TO HATE THAT SHIT. IRONIC, REALLY. MESSES WITH THEIR CIRCUITS, I GUESS.

IN THE PAST

SOPHOMORE YEAR OF COLLEGE

THREE OF US BELIEVE WE ALL HAVE THE ABILITY TO SHAPE THE WORLD AROUND US.

TWO THINK EXISTENCE OF CHOICE REFUTES ANY NON-FREE-WILL ARGUMENTS...

THAT'S FIVE OF YOU. WHAT ABOUT YOUR SIXTH?

IN ONE OF MY PHILOSOPHY CLASSES, THE PROFESSOR, THIS OLD PEDO GUY WITH ORGANIZED FILES OF KIDDY PORN ON HIS OFFICE COMPUTER, BROKE US OUT INTO GROUPS TO TALK ABOUT "FREE WILL".

MY GROUP ALL PATTED EACH OTHER'S BACKS AND I DISAGREED BECAUSE I'D READ A BOOK BEFORE. TRUE TO THEIR PROGRAMMING, THEY FOUGHT, FOR SOME REASON, FOR THEIR SHITTY IDEALS.

WHY DON'T YOU GO AHEAD, PSYCHO?

NEITHER MAKE ANY SENSE.

IT WAS HILARIOUS.

EXPLAIN, PLEASE.

WE HAVE NO CHOICE. I MEAN, IT'S LAUGHABLE TO THINK WE HAVE A CHOICE TO BREATHE OR EAT. WE HAVE TO DO THOSE THINGS. NEED IS NOT CHOICE. IT'S NEED.

OUR EXISTENCE IS POWERED AND MANAGED BY DESIRES AND WANTS AND NEEDS. GIVING IN TO THOSE THINGS, LIKE, RECOGNIZING THE NECESSITY OF THEM AND JUST DOING IT, IS NOT ONLY EASIER, IT'S MORE FULFILLING THAN BEING A DICK AND GOING AGAINST IT.

SO, PROFESSOR PEDO – I'M ALMOST 100% SURE ALL STUDENTS AND FACULTY CALLED HIM THAT – ASKED ME ABOUT SUICIDE. AND THE OTHER GROUPS WANTED TO LISTEN IN ON THIS SHIT EVEN MORE.

... AND SUICIDE IS CAUSED BY IMBALANCE, CHEMICALLY, IN THE BRAIN.

I FAIL TO SEE HOW THE MISFIRING OF NEURONS IN THE BRAIN ARE A CHOICE.

WHAT ABOUT BEING GAY? IS BEING GAY A CHOICE?

I CAN'T SEE HOW IT COULD BE.

THEN, PEDO PROF ASKED ME IF I'D HEARD THE TERM NIHILIST. BECAUSE, YOU KNOW, I'VE NEVER BEEN TO THE ATHEIST SUB-REDDIT.

AND, I MEAN, I TOOK A MINUTE, BECAUSE PAUSES MAKE YOU SOUND SMART. AS IF YOU'RE THINKING REAL DEEP AND SHIT.

YEAH. I'VE HEARD OF IT.

SO, DO YOU CONSIDER YOURSELF A NIHILIST?

HOW SAD IS IT THAT THEY PAY THIS GUY WHEN HE CAN'T EVEN PRESENT ALL SIDES OF AN ISSUE? "HI, I'M FIFTY-FOUR AND STILL GETTING MY DOCTORATE. CAN I FAIL AT TEACHING FOR YOUR INSTITUTE?"

NO.

AT THE MOMENT

MY BODY'S CLAN IS GONE, AND NOW I'M NEAR THAT FUCKING BASEBALL STADIUM.

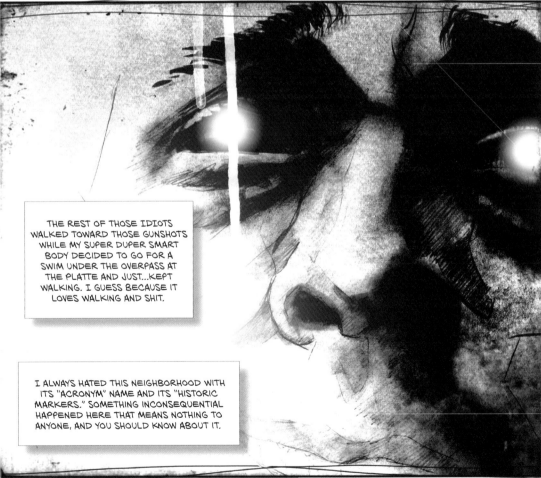

THE REST OF THOSE IDIOTS WALKED TOWARD THOSE GUNSHOTS WHILE MY SUPER DUPER SMART BODY DECIDED TO GO FOR A SWIM UNDER THE OVERPASS AT THE PLATTE AND JUST...KEPT WALKING. I GUESS BECAUSE IT LOVES WALKING AND SHIT.

I ALWAYS HATED THIS NEIGHBORHOOD WITH ITS "ACRONYM" NAME AND ITS "HISTORIC MARKERS." SOMETHING INCONSEQUENTIAL HAPPENED HERE THAT MEANS NOTHING TO ANYONE, AND YOU SHOULD KNOW ABOUT IT.

AND THEN I SPOT SOMETHING.

CHAPTER SIX :
LUST

AT THE MOMENT

THEIR CAMP MUST BE CLOSE. THEY WERE PEDALING AT FUCK SPEED.

GUESS THE CHASE IS ON.

AS A REASONABLE MAN, AND I'M SUPPOSING THAT YOU AGREE WITH MY SELF-DIGNOSIS, I NEED SEX AND THE WALLOP OF ADRENALINE... LOTS OF SEX AND ADRENALINE.

FOR MANY PRUDISH PEOPLE, THE MENTION OF GIVING INTO OUR CARNAL DESIRES IS SO LAUGHABLY FROWNED UPON.

WHO... IS THAT?

WE ALL CAME FROM SEX. WE FIND ULTIMATE PEACE IN SEX. AND WITHOUT SEX, LIFE IS, WELL, IT'S NOT MEANINGLESS, BUT SOMETHING LESS DRAMATIC THAN THAT.

DAMN BASTARDS... STAY OUT OF MY WAY.

WHAT THE...

HEY YOU. GUY UP THERE. I KNOW YOU!

WAIT. WHAT?

HOW IN THE...?

YOU KNOW ME? WHAT IS THIS, SOME PAST LIFE SHIT?

YEAH, MAN. YOU'RE JUST LIKE ME.

AND YET...THERE IS SOMETHING FAMILIAR.

THEN AGAIN, MAYBE I'M NOT THE ONLY ONE.

SO...

/FIRSTPERSONMODE, I GUESS.

GREAT, DUDE. NOW, YOU GOING TO HELP ME OR ARE WE GOING TO JERK EACH OTHER OFF?

UHH... YEAH.

YOU'RE IN CHARGE OF KEEPING THESE DUMBSHITS HERE. I NEED THEM FOR LATER.

FOR WHAT?

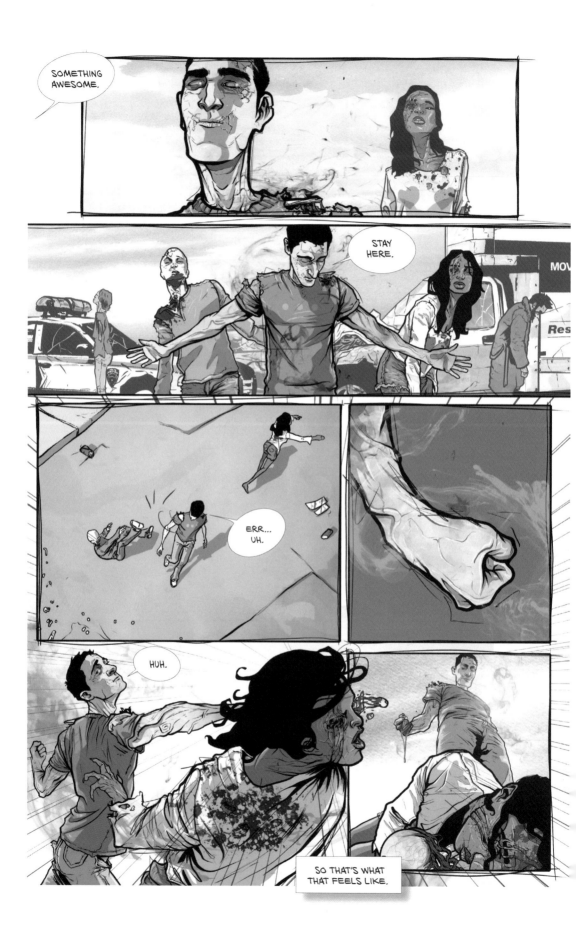

CHAPTER SEVEN:
CONNECT

I'M LUCKY ENOUGH TO HAVE THE RIGHT DNA OR WHAT HAVE YOU TO BE PREPARED FOR IT.

GOTTA GET OUT.

OH GOD!

AND PREPARATION MEANS OTHERS SHOULD BE SEEKING ME OUT, LOOKING FOR SHELTER IN THE STORM.

SHOOT!

THAT'S NOT WHAT I...

"THE WORLD BREAKS EVERYONE AND AFTERWARD MANY ARE STRONG AT THE BROKEN PLACES." READ *A FAREWELL TO ARMS*, TOO. HEMINGWAY MUST HAVE SEEN THE FUTURE.

I AM THAT SHELTER. THEY WILL COME TO ME.

MY FLOCK.

CHAPTER EIGHT:
NO NAME

AT THE MOMENT

GUY MCROCKCLIMBER *BRBS* INTO THE BUILDING, PUSHING THOSE OLD BODIES ALONG AND HERE I AM JUST STANDING.

WHAT AM I DOING OUT HERE?

I MEAN, WHAT DOES HE KNOW ABOUT ME? "STAY HERE AND GET USED TO CONTROLLING YOUR BODY," OR WHATEVER. NOT INTERESTED. NEVER WILL BE.

IT WAS COMFORTABLE THEN, WHEN I WAS, I DON'T KNOW, "ALIVE," I GUESS. MORE CALM.

KRAK KRAK KRAK KRAK

I USED TO GAME AS A PACIFIST SOMETIMES. I'M NOT A "GAMER" OR ANYTHING. I'D GO THROUGH THE MAP, NOT SHOOTING OR HITTING ANYTHING... SEE HOW FAR I COULD GET.

PISSED PEOPLE OFF.

IN THE PAST

JUNIOR YEAR OF HIGH SCHOOL

WHEN I WAS IN HIGH SCHOOL, THERE WERE THESE PIECES OF SHIT WHO WOULD TRY TO "BULLY" ME OR WHATEVER.

YOU HAVE TO CARE TO BE BULLIED. AND WHY SHOULD I CARE ABOUT SHITBRAINS?

THEY'D SAY SOMETHING. I'D *LOL*. AFTER A WHILE, THOUGH, I GOT BORED OF THOSE GAMES.

THOUGHT ABOUT "COLUMBINE-ING" IT. TOO MESSY. BUT THOSE GUYS DID *SOMETHING*, I GUESS, WHICH IS KINDA COOL.

YOUR MOM WAS TOTALLY AWESOME, MAN.

SHE WAS THE BEST. *BUHWAH*

MADE MORE SENSE TO STAY IN MY ELEMENT.

Status   Photo

Help me, everyone. Its hot in Hell.

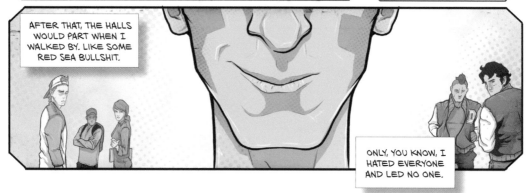

AFTER THAT, THE HALLS WOULD PART WHEN I WALKED BY. LIKE SOME RED SEA BULLSHIT.

ONLY, YOU KNOW, I HATED EVERYONE AND LED NO ONE.

IN THE PAST

A YEAR AGO

I WOULDN'T CALL GAMING OR TROLLING FUNNY. FUN, YES. I'D STAY UP TILL TWO MOST NIGHTS, MOSTLY TROLLING.

TROLLING ASSHOLES WHO ARE EASY TO PISS OFF ISN'T FUNNY, THOUGH. THEY'RE JUST THE WORST KIND OF PEOPLE. THE ONES WHO CARE TOO MUCH.

WATCHING PEOPLE'S ANGRY, FLAILING RESPONSES TO MY POSTS. 'KAY. MAYBE IT IS FUNNY.

MARIE WAS THE KIND OF DUMMY WHO BELIEVED THAT GRAND, MOVIE GESTURES HAPPENED IN REAL LIFE. YOU KNOW, THE ONES WHERE THE GIRL IS SITTING ON A PARK BENCH AND HER BOYFRIEND GETS DOWN ON ONE KNEE IN THE MUD TO PROPOSE.

DO YOU LOVE ME?

LOAD OF HORSESHIT.

I DON'T KNOW.

SHE ALWAYS DID HAVE A DIFFICULT TIME UNDERSTANDING WHAT I WAS ABOUT.

I'D SAY SOMETHING LIKE, "DO YOU WANT TO GET DINNER?" AND SHE'D TURN IT INTO, "DO YOU WANT TO MOVE IN TOGETHER?"

SHE'S A DOPE.

SHE SAID SHE'S "MY DOPE." GUESS THAT QUALIFIER'S IMPORTANT TO HER.

I'M NOT A TALKER. I LOVE TO WATCH THE MORONS AROUND ME TRY TO FIND THE RIGHT WORDS WHILE I LAUGH TO MYSELF.

DO YOU WANT TO GET MARRIED AFTER COLLEGE?

IF YOU WANT TO. IT DOESN'T REALLY MATTER.

DO YOU LOVE ME?

I DON'T KNOW. YES?

BUT MARIE LOVED TO TALK AND ASK INANE QUESTIONS THAT I COULD GIVE TWO SHITS ABOUT.

I DON'T KNOW. IF YOU WANT TO GET MARRIED, GET MARRIED.

SO, DO YOU WANT TO GET MARRIED OR NOT?

I DON'T KNOW. YES?

CHAPTER NINE: EVOLUTION

IF I KNEW THEN WHAT I KNOW NOW...

I WOULDN'T JUST HAVE SPENT MY TIME IN PURSUIT. I WOULD HAVE HELPED THEM TO BECOME SOMETHING TRULY TRANSCENDENTAL.

THEN AGAIN, PURSUIT IS 90% OF THE FUN.

CHAPTER TEN:
SUICIDE

AT THE MOMENT

NATURE. YEAH.

MAMAN WOULD TRY AND BRING ME OUT TO THE MOUNTAINS. SKIING AND SNOWBOARDING AND INJURIES AND A LACK OF OXYGEN. NO THANKS.

HE CALLS ME "BROTHER" A LOT, BUT HE'S NOT.

I GUESS, WE'RE SIMILAR OR WHATEVER. I DON'T CARE. I JUST LISTEN.

THIS IS JUST TOO CLICHÉ.

BATTERY'S DEAD.

THERE HAVE TO BE OTHER BATTERIES AROUND.

HOW LONG WILL IT TAKE TO FIND ONE AND REPLACE IT?

I DON'T REPAIR 'EM, MAN.

OF COURSE NOT. YOUR FIELD IS STEALING THEM, THEN?

HA! IF IT WEREN'T FOR ME "STEALING" THIS ONE, YOU'D ALL BE DEAD AND STILL IN DENVER.

IT'S LATE. WE CAN FIND A PLACE TO REST UP AND FUCKING FIX IT IN THE MORNING.

YOU KNOW THE AREA, ELI?

MY...I'VE SEEN SOME HOUSES HERE IN GENESEE. THEY'RE SKI HOUSES, SO THEY'RE PROBABLY EMPTY.

A THERAPIST ONCE TOLD ME I HOLD ONTO GRUDGES. BULLSHIT.

I LET GO WHEN I GET BACK AT THEM. NOT BEFORE. ONCE IT'S DONE, IT'S, LIKE, DONE.

CHAPTER ELEVEN:
WE

AT THE MOMENT

CHAPTER TWELVE: HOWL

AT THE MOMENT

HAS ANYONE SEEN ELI?

HEARD HOWLING LAST NIGHT. LIKE WHEN MITCH WOULD TALK TO THE NEIGHBOR'S DOGS.

NOPE.

HE COULDN'T HAVE LEFT.

I CHECKED ALL THE ROOMS. HE'S NOT HERE.

HEY BUDDY, HAVE YOU SEEN OUR MAN?

ELI? NOT SINCE LAST NIGHT.

WHAT DID YOU DO TO HIM?

I SAW HIM LEAVE. HE WAS MUTTERING SOMETHING ABOUT MAKING THINGS RIGHT.

DIDN'T DO ANYTHING.

MARIBETH, WE CAN'T STAY HERE. YOUR LEG WILL GET INFECTED AND WE CAN'T TREAT IT HERE. WE NEED TO FIND A DOCTOR'S OFFICE OR DRUG STORE OR SOMETHING – CRUTCHES.

I HAVE TO WATCH OUT FOR YOU TWO.

MARK...

YOU. I HAVE TO LOOK OUT FOR YOU.

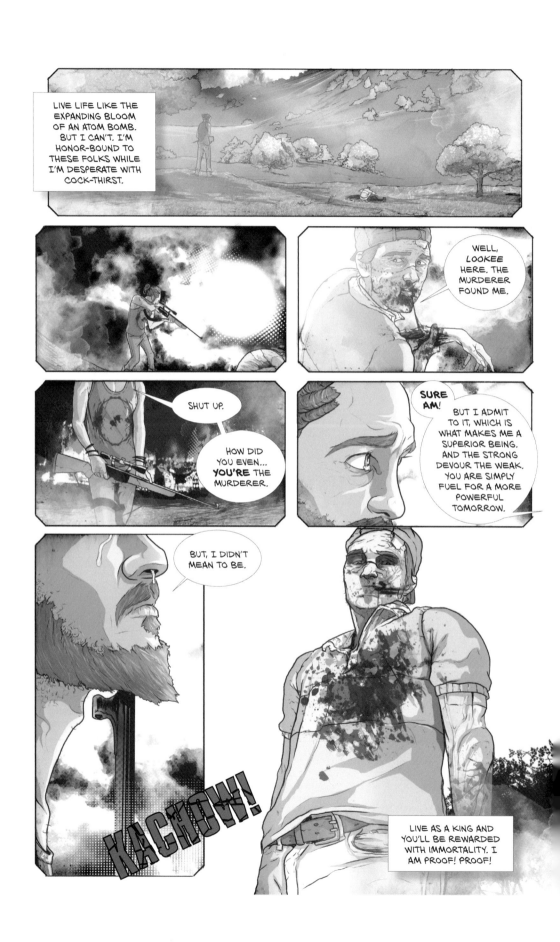

IN THE PAST

THOSE TWO GIRLS ON THE HIGHWAY REMIND ME OF MARIE. ALL EMPTY-HEADED AND ALL-AWARE.

IT WAS A NICE NIGHT, SHE TOLD ME. IT WAS HARD FOR ME TO NOTICE. TOO MUCH OTHER BULLSHIT TO THINK ABOUT.

SHE DIDN'T NOTICE THAT THE WORLD WAS ENDING, THOUGH. PEOPLE TELL ME I DON'T RECOGNIZE WHEN THINGS ARE GOING BAD. I GUESS FOR ME IT WAS JUST ANOTHER NIGHT.

OH MY GOD! WESTFALL! I LIVED HERE FRESHMAN YEAR. IT WAS AMAZING!

WE USED TO RUN ACROSS HERE IN OUR SWEATS AND GET BREAKFAST AT DURWARD.

ALL THE BOYS WERE ALWAYS STILL HUNG OVER, SO WE WOULD BRING BACK THOSE ONE WAFFLES WITH THE POWDERED SUGAR.

EXCEPT FOR WHEN I WAS BIT.

DON'T YOU REMEMBER?

NO.

HOW COULD YOU FORGET? IT'S COLLEGE. IT'S, LIKE, THE FORMATIVE TIME IN EVERYONE'S LIFE.

I GUESS. I NEVER THINK ABOUT IT...

IT WAS PAINFUL AND ALL, BUT WHAT ISN'T? YOUR DAD CALLS YOU A BASTARD AND SLAPS YOU AROUND. *THAT'S* PAINFUL.

RU... *GURGLE* ...RUN.

I'M NOT ONE OF THOSE FUCKING MONKS WHO CAN WALK ACROSS HOT COALS OR STAB HOLES THROUGH THEIR SKIN WITHOUT WINCING.

I'M USUALLY JUST COOL ABOUT PAIN, IS ALL.

BUT THIS WAS HARDER TO IGNORE.

MARIE?

AND THAT'S IT. THAT'S MY ORIGIN OR WHATEVER.

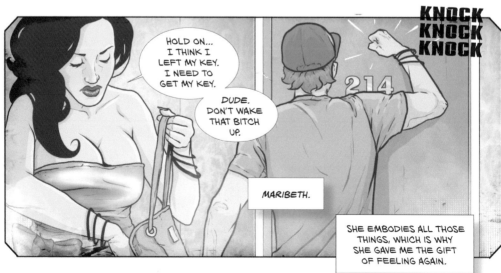

ZIPPPPPP

SHE SHOWED ME THE WAY TO LIVE THIS NEW LIFE.

AT THE MOMENT

WE CAN ALL LIVE IMMORTALLY. COMPLETELY.

YOU KILLED MY HUSBAND. THE FATHER OF MY... MY...YOU... FUCK YOU.

KSACKBOOM!

I WISH THERE WERE SOMETHING I COULD DO TO THANK HER.

YOU'VE THREATENED OR KILLED EVERYONE I'VE DEPENDED ON SINCE THE WORLD WENT TO SHIT.

HEY. LETS...I DON'T KNOW, BRING IT DOWN?

RIFLE'S ONLY GOT TWO SHOTS. AND NO SWEET TALK NEEDED. I KNOW YOU'RE THE LOVE OF MY LIFE.

NO ONE CARES ABOUT ANYONE ELSE. NO ONE REMEMBERS THAT THEY WERE SHITTY TO THE QUIET KID.

ZIIIIIIPP

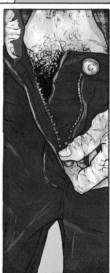

I...NO.

WHAT, I SHOULD JUST FORGIVE THEM?

FORGIVE THEM WHEN **THEY** SHOW NO REMORSE? FUCK YOU. **NO.**

I FEEL IT ALL. EVERYTHING. I'M AT ONE WITH THE UNIVERSE.

NOT TO SOUND CRASS, BUT I HAVEN'T FELT LIKE THIS SINCE THAT DEAD THING BIT ME. LIKE ACHIEVING ECSTASY A THOUSAND TIMES IN A ROW.

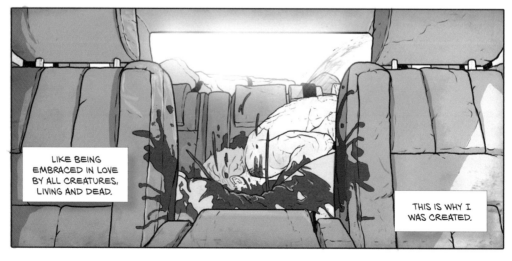

LIKE BEING EMBRACED IN LOVE BY ALL CREATURES, LIVING AND DEAD.

THIS IS WHY I WAS CREATED.

CHAPTER FIFTEEN: LINGER

NO.

HE'S MINE! THIS IS SUPPOSED TO BE MY REDEMPTION! YOU CAN'T TAKE THIS FROM ME.

WHAT THE FUCK ARE YOU YAPPIN' ABOUT, YOU SNIVELING BITCH?

DON'T...DON'T THREATEN MY FRIENDS.

CHAPTER SIXTEEN:
BEGINNINGS

AT THE MOMENT

PUSH A MAN TO GO OUTSIDE, RUN IN A GROUP OF LIKE-MINDED ASSES IN THE SUN, AND THIS IS WHAT YOU GET: SUBMISSION.

BUT THIS IS MY SUBMISSION. NO COWARDICE. JUST ANGER.

I NOW UNDERSTAND WHAT IT IS TO BE DETACHED, YET FULL OF ACTION. THERE IS BALANCE THERE. I AM THAT BALANCE.

AND MY FURY IS
HOT AS THE SUN.

DAVID FAROZ PRECHT

DAVID FAROZ PRECHT IS A COPYWRITER
AND COMIC BOOK WRITER. HIS SHORT
STORY 'VISUAL CUES' WAS FEATURED IN
'READING WITH PICTURES VOLUME I'.
'TETHERED' IS DAVID'S FIRST, FULL-LENGTH
PUBLISHED WORK. HE LIVES IN OAKLAND,
CALIFORNIA WITH HIS WIFE LINDSAY AND
CAN BE FOUND ONLINE AS @DAVIDPRECHT
ON TWITTER AND AT DAVIDPRECHT.COM.

DANNY LUCKERT

DANNY LUCKERT WAS BORN AND RAISED ON
LONG ISLAND AND STUDIED ILLUSTRATION AT
THE SCHOOL OF VISUAL ARTS. HIS PUBLISHED
COMIC BOOK WORKS INCLUDE 'PRIMARY
VECTOR' (ONLINE, SELF PUBLISHED),
'ELECTRONIC' (VIP COMICS) AND 'HAUNTED'
(RED5COMICS). CURRENTLY, HE IS WORKING
ON A CREATOR-OWNED MINISERIES
WITH WRITER CULLEN BUNN ('MAGNETO'/
'SINESTRO'/ '6TH GUN') AS WELL AS THE
SEQUEL TO 'HAUNTED' WITH RED5COMICS.

LINDSAY MCCOMB

LINDSAY MCCOMB IS A WRITER, EDITOR AND
DESIGNER WHO HAS CONTRIBUTED WRITING
AND DESIGN WORK TO SEVERAL ONLINE
PUBLICATIONS INCLUDING SOULPANCAKE,
SMASHING MAGAZINE, META Q AND NINETEEN
MONTHS. SHE HAS A BACKGROUND IN
TECHNICAL JOURNALISM AND IS CURRENTLY
PURSUING AN MBA IN DESIGN STRATEGY AT
CALIFORNIA COLLEGE OF ARTS. HER WORK CAN
BE FOUND ONLINE AT LINDSAYMCCOMB.COM.

CPSIA information can be obtained at www.ICGtesting.com
Printed in the USA
BVIW12n0054230816
459630BV00004B/2